Contents

Mathematics

+	addition	$\triangle$	triangle
−	subtraction	$\cup$	union
×	multiplication	$\cap$	intersection
÷	division	π	pi (≈3.14)
>	greater than	{[()]}	brackets
≥	greater than or equal to	∞	infinity
<	less than	#	number
≤	less than or equal to	∴	therefore
=	equal to	∵	because
≠	not equal to	%	per cent
≈	approximately equal to	√	square root
°	degree	.	decimal point
∠	angle	:	ratio
⌐	right angle	c	cent
⊥	is perpendicular to	€	euro
‖	parallel	p	pence
≅	is congruent to	£	pound

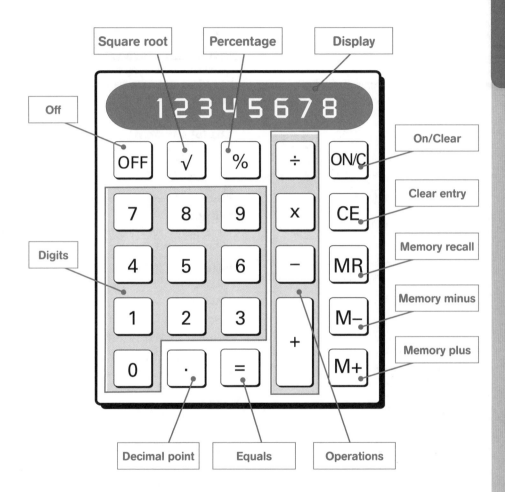

Square root

Percentage

Display

Off

On/Clear

Clear entry

Memory recall

Digits

Memory minus

Memory plus

Decimal point

Equals

Operations

A

abacus
a device for calculating; can use beads or counters

acute
describes an angle between 0° and 90°

addend
any number which is to be added;
e.g. 2 + 5 = 7 (2 and 5 are addends)

addition
a mathematical operation; e.g. 3 + 4

adjacent
adjoining (as used to describe lines and angles)

alternate
every other one in a sequence

angle
the space between two intersecting lines on surfaces, near where they meet, in degrees

anticlockwise
moving in the opposite direction from the hands on a clock

arbitrary units
non-standard units such as hand spans, counters and hand claps

arc
part of the circumference of a circle

area
the amount of space within a perimeter (expressed in square units)

array
the arrangement of the units of a number in rows and columns; e.g. 6 = : : :

arrow diagram
a diagram used to display various possible choices

ascending order
the arrangement of numbers from smallest to largest

attribute
a characteristic of an object; a way to classify objects; e.g. round, red, thick

average (see 'mean')
a number representing a set of numbers (obtained by dividing the total of the numbers by the number of numbers in the set)

axis (of symmetry)
a line dividing a shape into two symmetrical parts

B

bar graph
a diagram representing information by the length of bars

base
the line or face on which a shape is standing

block graph
a diagram representing information by the length of blocks

C

capacity
the amount of space in the interior of an object (the amount of liquid/air it contains)

Carroll diagram
a problem-solving diagram used in classification activities

chord
line segment connecting two points on the arc of a circle

chronological
describes dates arranged in the order in which they occur; e.g. 1920, 1936, 1992

Important mathematical terms

circumference
the distance around a circle (its perimeter)

classification
the arrangement of objects into groups according to attributes

clockwise
moving in the same direction as the hands on a clock

closed curve
a shape with no end points

common numeral
the symbol commonly used to represent a mathematical expression; e.g. the common numeral for 10^3 is 1000

commutative law
the order in which two numbers are added or multiplied does not affect the result; e.g. $3 + 7 = 7 + 3$ and $4 \times 6 = 6 \times 4$; this is not the same for subtraction and division

complementary addition
the complement is the amount needed to complete a set. 'Counting on' to a higher total; e.g. the way change is given after a purchase. The method of 'subtracting' which changes the subtraction to an addition; e.g. $7 - 3 = \_$ 'is the same as' $3 + \_ = 7$

composite number
a number which can be divided by more than itself and 1; e.g. 4, 6, 8, 9, 12

concentric circles
circles which have the same centre point

congruent
congruent shapes are the same shape and size (equal)

consecutive
consecutive numbers follow in order without interruption; e.g. 11, 12, 13

constant
adding, subtracting, multiplying or dividing by the same amount each time

coordinates
numbers used to locate a point on a grid

cubic
a cubic number is the answer when the square of a number is multiplied by the number itself

cylinder
a circular prism with two congruent, parallel and circular end faces

D

decimal notation
the expression of a numeral in a form which uses the decimal place value system; e.g. 13.5

denominator
the number below the line in a fraction

descending order
the arrangement of numbers from largest to smallest

diagonal
a straight line connecting two non-adjacent vertices (corners) of a polygon

diameter
a straight line connecting two points on the circumference of a circle and passing through the circle's centre

difference
by how much a number is bigger or smaller than another

digit
any whole number from 0 to 9 (inclusive)

digital clock
a clock that shows the time by using numbers rather than hands

Important mathematical terms

dimensions
the measurements of a shape; e.g. length, width, height

distributive law
to multiply a sum by a number is the same as multiplying each addend by the number and then adding the products; e.g.
$3 \times (4+2) = (3 \times 4) + (3 \times 2) = 12 + 6 = 18$

dividend
a number which is to be divided by another number; e.g. $21 \div 3$ (the dividend is 21)

divisible
a number is divisible by another number if the second number is a factor of the first; e.g. 6 is divisible by 2 because 2 is a factor of 6

division
the inverse operation of multiplication; e.g. $21 \div 7 = 3$
repeated subtraction can also be used to achieve the same result;
e.g. $21 \underline{-7-7-7}$
$\overline{}3$

divisor
a number which is to be divided into another number; e.g. $21 \div 3$ (3 is the divisor)

dodecagon
a polygon with 12 sides and 12 angles

dodecahedron
a three-dimensional shape with 12 faces

doubling
multiplying a number or shape by two

E

edge
the intersection of two faces of a three-dimensional object

equality
having the same value

equation
a statement of equality between two expressions; e.g. $3 \times 4 = 6 + 6$

equilateral triangle
a triangle with congruent (equal) sides and angles

even number
a positive (e.g. 8) or negative (e.g. –6) number exactly divisible by two

F

face
a plane surface of a three-dimensional object

face value
the numeral itself despite its position in a number; e.g. the face value of the 5 in 3520 is 5

factor
a number which will divide evenly into another

factorisation
to represent a counting number as the product of counting numbers;
e.g. $24 = 4 \times 6$; 8×3; 12×2; 24×1
To show 24 as a product of its prime factors, it would look like this: $24 = 2 \times 2 \times 2 \times 3$

fraction
an amount expressed in terms of a numerator and a denominator (usually part of a whole)

H

heft
to test the weight of objects by lifting them in the hands and comparing them

height
the highest part of the shape from the base

heptagon
a polygon with seven sides and seven angles

hexagon
a polygon with six sides and six angles

hexagonal
having the shape of a hexagon

hexahedron
a three-dimensional shape with six faces

horizontal
describes a line or plane parallel to the horizon

I

improper fraction
a fraction whose numerator is equal to or greater than its denominator

index notation
a short way of writing large numbers by multiplication of repeated factors; e.g. 3^2

inequality
not having the same value

infinity
having no limit, endless, impossible to measure. The symbol used for infinity is ∞. It is a word used to describe a situation that has no end, such as:
- the number of ways you can paint a painting
- counting from 1, 2, 3, 4, ... to infinity
- travelling into space

integer
a negative or positive whole number; e.g. ... −2, −1, 0, 1, 2 ...

intersection
the point or line where two lines or two faces meet or, in set theory, those elements common to two or more sets

inverse operation
opposite operations; addition and subtraction are inverse operations; multiplication and division are inverse operations; halving and doubling are also inverse operations

irregular shapes
shapes which do not have all congruent sides and all congruent angles

isosceles triangle
a triangle with two congruent sides and two congruent angles

L

length
the distance measured from end to end

line graph
a diagram using straight lines to join points representing certain information

line segment
part of a line between two given points

M

mass
the amount of matter in an object (its weight on Earth)

mean (arithmetic mean)
the average of a set of numbers

median
in statistics, the middle measurement when information is arranged in order of size; e.g. 5 is the median of 2, 3, 5, 10, 13. Where there is no middle score, an average of the two central scores is taken

mixed numeral
a symbol representing a whole number and a fraction; e.g. $2^3/_8$

Important mathematical terms

modal score (mode)

in statistics, the measurement that occurs most often; e.g. the modal score of 2, 7, 4, 4, 3, 4, 9, 4 is 4

model

a representation of an object preserving the significant features

multiples

the multiples of a number are those numbers which a given number will divide into exactly; e.g. some multiples of 3 are 3, 6, 9, 12 etc.

multiplication

a mathematical operation; e.g. 2 x 7. Repeated addition can also be used to achieve the same result; e.g. 2 + 2 + 2 + 2 + 2 + 2

N

net

a flat pattern that can be folded to make a three-dimensional model of a shape

network

a system of lines (paths) and nodes (points representing intersections)

number

an indication of quantity

number line

a line on which equally spaced points are marked; points correspond, in order, to the integers

number sentence

a mathematical sentence that uses numbers and operation symbols; e.g. 6 + 7 = 13

numeral

a symbol used to represent a number; e.g. 5 and V are symbols representing the number 5

numerator

the number above the line in a fraction

O

obtuse angle

an angle between 90° and 180°

octagon

a polygon with eight sides and eight angles

octahedron

a polyhedron (three-dimensional shape) with eight faces

odd number

a number that leaves a remainder of 1 (when divided by 2)

operation

the four operations of arithmetic: addition, subtraction, multiplication and division

ordinal number

a number which indicates position in an ordered sequence; e.g. first, second, third

outcome

a result

P

parallel lines

lines with no common points and always the same distance apart

parallelogram

a four-sided polygon with opposite sides equal and parallel and containing no right angles

partitioning

a method of simplifying a problem in order to calculate the solution; e.g. 43 + 54 = (40 + 50) + (3 + 4) = 90 + 7 = 97

path

a line connecting nodes (points) in a network

pattern

a repeated design

Important mathematical terms

pentagon
a polygon with five sides and five angles

pentomino
a plane shape made of five congruent squares connected to each other by at least one common side

percentage
a quantity expressed in hundredths (%)

perfect number
a number which is the sum of its factors excluding itself; e.g. 6 = 1 + 2 + 3.

perimeter
the length of the distance around the boundary of a shape

perpendicular line
a line at right angles to another line or plane

pi (π)
the ratio of the circumference of a circle to its diameter; approximately 3.14

pictogram
a graph in which data is represented by pictures. One picture could represent one unit or many

pie chart
a circular graph in which sectors of a circle are used to show information

place value
indicates the position of a numeral; e.g. the place value of the 3 in the number 357 is hundreds

plane
a surface which is flat and has no boundaries

polygon
a two-dimensional shape with three or more straight lines

polyhedron (plural – polyhedra)
a three-dimensional shape with plane faces

prime factor
a prime number that will divide exactly into another number; e.g. 2 and 3 are prime factors of 6

prime number
a number with only two factors: 1 and itself

prism
a three-dimensional shape with at least one pair of opposite faces which are congruent and parallel

probability
the likelihood of a particular outcome in a chance event

product
the result when two or more numbers are multiplied; e.g. the product of 2, 3 and 4 is 2 x 3 x 4 = 24

**proper fraction
(vulgar or common fraction)**
a fraction in which the numerator is less than the denominator

property
an attribute of a two-dimensional or three-dimensional shape

protractor
a semicircular or circular instrument for measuring angles

pyramid
a three-dimensional shape made up of a base shape such as a triangle, square, hexagon or decagon. The opposite end of the shape forms a point called an apex

Q

quadrant
a quarter of the area of a circle which also contains a right angle

quadrilateral
any four-sided polygon

R

radius

a line joining the centre of a circle to a point on the circle's circumference

range

the difference between the greatest and least values in a set of data

rectangle

a quadrilateral with opposite sides equal and parallel and containing four right angles (a square is a rectangle)

reflex angle

an angle greater than 180°

region

the interior area enclosed by a perimeter (the area outside the perimeter is the exterior region)

regular shape

a polygon is regular if all its sides and angles are congruent (opposite – irregular)

repeating

the pattern uses the same symbols or pictures over and over; e.g. 3, 4, 3, 4, 3 ...

rhombus

a parallelogram with congruent sides and containing no right angles (a 'diamond' shape)

right angle

an angle containing 90°

right-angled triangle

a triangle containing one right angle (90°)

rotating

turning in a clockwise or anticlockwise direction

rule of order

a rule used for performing operations in expressions which have more than one operation to ensure calculations are handled in the same way

S

scale

to change an amount according to a fixed proportion, either larger or smaller

scalene triangle

a triangle with sides of different length and three different interior angles

section

a flat surface made by cutting through a solid in any direction

sector

the part of a circle bounded by two radiuses and the included arc

segment

the part of a circle bounded by a chord and an arc

semicircle

half a circle (the area bounded by a diameter and an arc)

sequence

a set of numbers or objects arranged in some order

side

the edge of a 2-D shape

similar

two shapes are similar when they have the same shape but are different in size

simplify

to change to simpler terms; e.g. $^{45}/_{60}$ to $^{3}/_{4}$

solid shape

a three-dimensional shape (with length, width, height)

sphere

a three-dimensional shape comprising a set of points, each point being equidistant from its centre; e.g. a ball

square number

a number whose units can be arranged into a square; e.g. 4 :: ;
it is also the product of any number multiplied by itself

square pyramid

a three-dimensional shape with a square base and four sloping triangular sides meeting at a common vertex

squared

a number squared is multiplied by itself

subtraction

a mathematical operation; e.g. $27 - 4 = 23$

subtrahend (also minuend)

a number from which another number is to be subtracted; e.g. $25 - 6 = 19$ (25 is the subtrahend)

sum

the result when two or more numbers are added

supplementary angles

two angles which, when added, total 180°

surface area

the total area of all faces of a three-dimensional shape (measured in square units)

symmetry–plane

a line or plane divides a two- or three-dimensional shape or object so that the two sections are a mirror image of each other

symmetry–rotational

when a two- or three-dimensional shape or object can be rotated up to 360° around a point, making a mirror image of the original shape or object

T

tally

a record of items using vertical and oblique lines to represent each item

tangram

a Chinese puzzle made of a square cut into seven pieces. All seven pieces can be rearranged to make shapes and pictures

tessellating shapes

shapes which cover an area with no gaps between them; e.g. squares

tessellation

a repeating pattern of congruent shapes that completely cover an area leaving no gaps

tetrahedron

a polyhedron with four faces; e.g. triangular pyramid

tetromino

a plane shape made of four congruent squares connected to each other by at least one common side

three-dimensional shape

a shape with length, width and height

total

the result when two or more numbers are added

trapezium

a quadrilateral plane figure in which only one pair of opposite sides is parallel

trapezoid

a quadrilateral plane figure of which no two sides are parallel

traversable

a network is traversable if all paths can be traced over without going over the same path twice

Important mathematical terms

Mathematics – terms

tree diagram
these are used for classification activities or to show possible outcomes of chance events

triangular number
a number whose units can be arranged into a triangle; e.g. 6 •••

twin primes
prime numbers separated by a composite number; e.g. 3, 4, 5

V

Venn diagram
a diagram which shows sets and their relationships

vertex (plural – vertices)
the point at which two or more line segments or two or more edges of a polyhedron meet

vertical
a line or plane which is at right angles to the horizon

vinculum
the line which separates the numerator and the denominator in a fraction

volume
the amount of space taken up by an object

W

whole number
the numbers 0, 1, 2, 3, 4 … are called whole numbers

width
the distance from one side to another; the breadth

Other words of interest

To help understand addition and subtraction facts always remember, just like multiplication and division, if you know one fact then you will know several others.

> *For example:*
> *If you know ...*
>
> $$4 + 5 = 9$$
>
> *then you will also know ...*
>
> $5 + 4 = 9$ $9 - 5 = 4$ $9 - 4 = 5$

This table will help you with all your addition and subtraction facts to 20.

+	0	1	2	3	4	5	6	7	8	9	10
0	0	1	2	3	4	5	6	7	8	9	10
1	1	2	3	4	5	6	7	8	9	10	11
2	2	3	4	5	6	7	8	9	10	11	12
3	3	4	5	6	7	8	9	10	11	12	13
4	4	5	6	7	8	9	10	11	12	13	14
5	5	6	7	8	9	10	11	12	13	14	15
6	6	7	8	9	10	11	12	13	14	15	16
7	7	8	9	10	11	12	13	14	15	16	17
8	8	9	10	11	12	13	14	15	16	17	18
9	9	10	11	12	13	14	15	16	17	18	19
10	10	11	12	13	14	15	16	17	18	19	20

Multiplication and division facts

Mathematics – number

Multiplication and division facts are linked. If you know one multiplication fact, you will also know three other related facts.

> *For example:*
> *If you know ...*
> $$5 \times 3 = 15$$
> *then you will also know ...*
> $$3 \times 5 = 15 \qquad 15 \div 3 = 5 \qquad 15 \div 5 = 3$$

The following tables include the times tables and other facts you will learn at the same time.

2 x table	Other facts I know ...		
$1 \times 2 = 2$	$2 \times 1 = 2$	$2 \div 2 = 1$	$2 \div 1 = 2$
$2 \times 2 = 4$		$4 \div 2 = 2$	
$3 \times 2 = 6$	$2 \times 3 = 6$	$6 \div 2 = 3$	$6 \div 3 = 2$
$4 \times 2 = 8$	$2 \times 4 = 8$	$8 \div 2 = 4$	$8 \div 4 = 2$
$5 \times 2 = 10$	$2 \times 5 = 10$	$10 \div 2 = 5$	$10 \div 5 = 2$
$6 \times 2 = 12$	$2 \times 6 = 12$	$12 \div 2 = 6$	$12 \div 6 = 2$
$7 \times 2 = 14$	$2 \times 7 = 14$	$14 \div 2 = 7$	$14 \div 7 = 2$
$8 \times 2 = 16$	$2 \times 8 = 16$	$16 \div 2 = 8$	$16 \div 8 = 2$
$9 \times 2 = 18$	$2 \times 9 = 18$	$18 \div 2 = 9$	$18 \div 9 = 2$
$10 \times 2 = 20$	$2 \times 10 = 20$	$20 \div 2 = 10$	$20 \div 10 = 2$

3 x table

3 x table	Other facts I know ...		
1 x 3 = 3	3 x 1 = 3	3 ÷ 3 = 1	3 ÷ 1 = 3
2 x 3 = 6	3 x 2 = 6	6 ÷ 3 = 2	6 ÷ 2 = 3
3 x 3 = 9		9 ÷ 3 = 3	
4 x 3 = 12	3 x 4 = 12	12 ÷ 3 = 4	12 ÷ 4 = 3
5 x 3 = 15	3 x 5 = 15	15 ÷ 3 = 5	15 ÷ 5 = 3
6 x 3 = 18	3 x 6 = 18	18 ÷ 3 = 6	18 ÷ 6 = 3
7 x 3 = 21	3 x 7 = 21	21 ÷ 3 = 7	21 ÷ 7 = 3
8 x 3 = 24	3 x 8 = 24	24 ÷ 3 = 8	24 ÷ 8 = 3
9 x 3 = 27	3 x 9 = 27	27 ÷ 3 = 9	27 ÷ 9 = 3
10 x 3 = 30	3 x 10 = 30	30 ÷ 3 = 10	30 ÷ 10 = 3

4 x table

4 x table	Other facts I know ...		
1 x 4 = 4	4 x 1 = 4	4 ÷ 4 = 1	4 ÷ 1 = 4
2 x 4 = 8	4 x 2 = 8	8 ÷ 4 = 2	8 ÷ 2 = 4
3 x 4 = 12	4 x 3 = 12	12 ÷ 4 = 3	12 ÷ 3 = 4
4 x 4 = 16		16 ÷ 4 = 4	
5 x 4 = 20	4 x 5 = 20	20 ÷ 4 = 5	20 ÷ 5 = 4
6 x 4 = 24	4 x 6 = 24	24 ÷ 4 = 6	24 ÷ 6 = 4
7 x 4 = 28	4 x 7 = 28	28 ÷ 4 = 7	28 ÷ 7 = 4
8 x 4 = 32	4 x 8 = 32	32 ÷ 4 = 8	32 ÷ 8 = 4
9 x 4 = 36	4 x 9 = 36	36 ÷ 4 = 9	36 ÷ 9 = 4
10 x 4 = 40	4 x 10 = 40	40 ÷ 4 = 10	40 ÷ 10 = 4

Multiplication and division facts

Mathematics – number

5 x table
1 x 5 = 5
2 x 5 = 10
3 x 5 = 15
4 x 5 = 20
5 x 5 = 25
6 x 5 = 30
7 x 5 = 35
8 x 5 = 40
9 x 5 = 45
10 x 5 = 50

Other facts I know …

5 x 1 = 5	5 ÷ 5 = 1	5 ÷ 1 = 5
5 x 2 = 10	10 ÷ 5 = 2	10 ÷ 2 = 5
5 x 3 = 15	15 ÷ 5 = 3	15 ÷ 3 = 5
5 x 4 = 20	20 ÷ 5 = 4	20 ÷ 4 = 5
	25 ÷ 5 = 5	
5 x 6 = 30	30 ÷ 5 = 6	30 ÷ 6 = 5
5 x 7 = 35	35 ÷ 5 = 7	35 ÷ 7 = 5
5 x 8 = 40	40 ÷ 5 = 8	40 ÷ 8 = 5
5 x 9 = 45	45 ÷ 5 = 9	45 ÷ 9 = 5
5 x 10 = 50	50 ÷ 5 = 10	50 ÷ 10 = 5

6 x table
1 x 6 = 6
2 x 6 = 12
3 x 6 = 18
4 x 6 = 24
5 x 6 = 30
6 x 6 = 36
7 x 6 = 42
8 x 6 = 48
9 x 6 = 54
10 x 6 = 60

Other facts I know …

6 x 1 = 6	6 ÷ 6 = 1	6 ÷ 1 = 6
6 x 2 = 12	12 ÷ 6 = 2	12 ÷ 2 = 6
6 x 3 = 18	18 ÷ 6 = 3	18 ÷ 3 = 6
6 x 4 = 24	24 ÷ 6 = 4	24 ÷ 4 = 6
6 x 5 = 30	30 ÷ 6 = 5	30 ÷ 5 = 6
	36 ÷ 6 = 6	
6 x 7 = 42	42 ÷ 6 = 7	42 ÷ 7 = 6
6 x 8 = 48	48 ÷ 6 = 8	48 ÷ 8 = 6
6 x 9 = 54	54 ÷ 6 = 9	54 ÷ 9 = 6
6 x 10 = 60	60 ÷ 6 = 10	60 ÷ 10 = 6

7 x table

7 x table
1 x 7 = 7
2 x 7 = 14
3 x 7 = 21
4 x 7 = 28
5 x 7 = 35
6 x 7 = 42
7 x 7 = 49
8 x 7 = 56
9 x 7 = 63
10 x 7 = 70

Other facts I know ...

7 x 1 = 7	7 ÷ 7 = 1	7 ÷ 1 = 7
7 x 2 = 14	14 ÷ 7 = 2	14 ÷ 2 = 7
7 x 3 = 21	21 ÷ 7 = 3	21 ÷ 3 = 7
7 x 4 = 28	28 ÷ 7 = 4	28 ÷ 4 = 7
7 x 5 = 35	35 ÷ 7 = 5	35 ÷ 5 = 7
7 x 6 = 42	42 ÷ 7 = 6	42 ÷ 6 = 7
	49 ÷ 7 = 7	
7 x 8 = 56	56 ÷ 7 = 8	56 ÷ 8 = 7
7 x 9 = 63	63 ÷ 7 = 9	63 ÷ 9 = 7
7 x 10 = 70	70 ÷ 7 = 10	70 ÷ 10 = 7

8 x table

8 x table
1 x 8 = 8
2 x 8 = 16
3 x 8 = 24
4 x 8 = 32
5 x 8 = 40
6 x 8 = 48
7 x 8 = 56
8 x 8 = 64
9 x 8 = 72
10 x 8 = 80

Other facts I know ...

8 x 1 = 8	8 ÷ 8 = 1	8 ÷ 1 = 8
8 x 2 = 16	16 ÷ 8 = 2	16 ÷ 2 = 8
8 x 3 = 24	24 ÷ 8 = 3	24 ÷ 3 = 8
8 x 4 = 32	32 ÷ 8 = 4	32 ÷ 4 = 8
8 x 5 = 40	40 ÷ 8 = 5	40 ÷ 5 = 8
8 x 6 = 48	48 ÷ 8 = 6	48 ÷ 6 = 8
8 x 7 = 56	56 ÷ 8 = 7	56 ÷ 7 = 8
	64 ÷ 8 = 8	
8 x 9 = 72	72 ÷ 8 = 9	72 ÷ 9 = 8
8 x 10 = 80	80 ÷ 8 = 10	80 ÷ 10 = 8

Multiplication and division facts

Mathematics – number

9 x table
1 x 9 = 9
2 x 9 = 18
3 x 9 = 27
4 x 9 = 36
5 x 9 = 45
6 x 9 = 54
7 x 9 = 63
8 x 9 = 72
9 x 9 = 81
10 x 9 = 90

Other facts I know ...		
9 x 1 = 9	9 ÷ 9 = 1	9 ÷ 1 = 9
9 x 2 = 18	18 ÷ 9 = 2	18 ÷ 2 = 9
9 x 3 = 27	27 ÷ 9 = 3	27 ÷ 3 = 9
9 x 4 = 36	36 ÷ 9 = 4	36 ÷ 4 = 9
9 x 5 = 45	45 ÷ 9 = 5	45 ÷ 5 = 9
9 x 6 = 54	54 ÷ 9 = 6	54 ÷ 6 = 9
9 x 7 = 63	63 ÷ 9 = 7	63 ÷ 7 = 9
9 x 8 = 72	72 ÷ 9 = 8	72 ÷ 8 = 9
	81 ÷ 9 = 9	
9 x 10 = 90	90 ÷ 9 = 10	90 ÷ 10 = 9

10 x table
1 x 10 = 10
2 x 10 = 20
3 x 10 = 30
4 x 10 = 40
5 x 10 = 50
6 x 10 = 60
7 x 10 = 70
8 x 10 = 80
9 x 10 = 90
10 x 10 = 100

Other facts I know ...		
10 x 1 = 10	10 ÷ 10 = 1	10 ÷ 1 = 10
10 x 2 = 20	20 ÷ 10 = 2	20 ÷ 2 = 10
10 x 3 = 30	30 ÷ 10 = 3	30 ÷ 3 = 10
10 x 4 = 40	40 ÷ 10 = 4	40 ÷ 4 = 10
10 x 5 = 50	50 ÷ 10 = 5	50 ÷ 5 = 10
10 x 6 = 60	60 ÷ 10 = 6	60 ÷ 6 = 10
10 x 7 = 70	70 ÷ 10 = 7	70 ÷ 7 = 10
10 x 8 = 80	80 ÷ 10 = 8	80 ÷ 8 = 10
10 x 9 = 90	90 ÷ 10 = 9	90 ÷ 9 = 10
	100 ÷ 10 = 10	

Basic facts repeat themselves throughout each of the number groupings.

> *For example:*
> *2 x 3 = 6* *is found in the two times table.*
> *It is also found in the three times table.*

This makes one less table or basic fact you need to learn.

This happens more and more as you move up the tables and, because of this, assuming the one times table and ten times table are excluded, there are only 36 actual multiplication facts you need to learn in order to know all of your tables. These are listed below.

2 x 2 = 4					
3 x 2 = 6					
4 x 2 = 8					
5 x 2 = 10	3 x 3 = 9				
6 x 2 = 12	4 x 3 = 12				
7 x 2 = 14	5 x 3 = 15				
8 x 2 = 16	6 x 3 = 18	4 x 4 = 16			
9 x 2 = 18	7 x 3 = 21	5 x 4 = 20			
	8 x 3 = 24	6 x 4 = 24			
	9 x 3 = 27	7 x 4 = 28	5 x 5 = 25		
		8 x 4 = 32	6 x 5 = 30		
		9 x 4 = 36	7 x 5 = 35		
			8 x 5 = 40	6 x 6 = 36	
	7 x 7 = 49		9 x 5 = 45	7 x 6 = 42	
	8 x 7 = 56			8 x 6 = 48	
	9 x 7 = 63			9 x 6 = 54	
		8 x 8 = 64			
		9 x 8 = 72			
			9 x 9 = 81		

Special numbers

Even numbers

A positive (e.g. 8) or negative (e.g. −8) number exactly divisible by two.

Examples of even numbers are: 2, 4, 6, 8, 10 and so on.

Odd numbers

A number that leaves a remainder of 1 when divided by 2.

Examples of odd numbers are: 3, 5, 7, 9, 11 and so on.

Prime numbers

A number that can be divided evenly by only 1 and itself.

Examples of prime numbers are: 2, 3, 5, 7, 11, 13, 17 and so on.

Composite numbers

A number that can be divided by more than itself and 1.

Examples of composite numbers are: 4, 6, 8, 9, 10, 12, 14 and so on.

Multiples

A multiple is the product of a number multiplied by another whole number.

For example: the multiples of 5 are: 5, 10, 15, 20, 25, 30, 35, 40, 45 and so on.

Factors

A number that will divide evenly into that number.

All numbers except 1 have more than one factor.

For example: 12 is the number The factors are 1, 2, 3, 4, 6, 12 and so on.

A prime factor is a prime number that will divide evenly into a given number.

For example: 2, 3 and 5 are prime factors of 30.

Counting numbers can be represented as a product of counting numbers by factorisation.

For example: 24 = 4 x 6; 8 x 3; 12 x 2; 24 x 1.

To show 24 as a product of its prime factors, it would look like this: *24 = 2 x 2 x 2 x 3.*

Index notation

Power or index notation is a short way of writing large numbers by multiplication of repeated factors.

The power of any number is also called index or exponential notation.

For example:
8^2 is the same as 8 x 8
8^3 is the same as 8 x 8 x 8
8^5 is the same as 8 x 8 x 8 x 8 x 8

exponent
base

Index notation is also called power as this is the word used to describe a number.

For example:
8^2 is called 8 to the power of two (also called 8 squared)
8^3 is called 8 to the power of three (also called 8 cubed)
8^5 is called 8 to the power of five
and so on...

Place value

Place value indicates the 'position of a numeral'.

For example:

4032.87

4 thousands, 0 hundreds, 3 tens, 2 ones, 8 tenths, 7 hundredths

Th	H	T	O	•	Tths	Hths
4	0	3	2	•	8	7

Decimals

The decimal number system is based on the number 10.

The decimal place system is based on multiples of ten where a whole number is divided into tenths, hundredths, thousandths and so on.

This diagram shows how we use decimal fractions or the decimal place system.

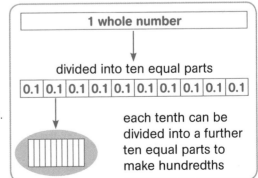

1 whole number

divided into ten equal parts

| 0.1 | 0.1 | 0.1 | 0.1 | 0.1 | 0.1 | 0.1 | 0.1 | 0.1 | 0.1 |

each tenth can be divided into a further ten equal parts to make hundredths

Fractions

Mathematics – number

A fraction is a number which usually represents a part of a whole number.
It is made up of:

- a denominator, which is the number below
  the line indicating how many parts the
  whole number is divided into.

- a numerator, which is the number above
  the line indicating how many parts are
  under consideration.

- a vinculum is the name of the line dividing
  the numerator and denominator.

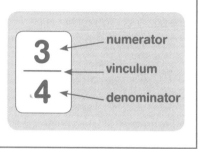

There are different types of fractions. These are:

- A proper fraction is a fraction where the value of
  the numerator is smaller than the denominator.

  For example: $^1/_2$

- An improper fraction is a fraction where the
  numerator is larger than the denominator.

  For example: $^4/_3$

- A mixed number is both a whole number and a
  proper fraction.

  For example: $1^2/_3$

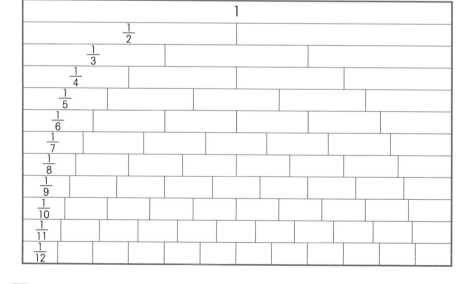

Percentages

A percentage is a number or quality represented in hundredths.

> *For example:*
> *If you achieve 8 correct answers out of a possible 10 (in a spelling test), your percentage is 80%.*

To convert a number or fraction to a percentage it is necessary to multiply the number by 100.

> *For example:*
> $$\frac{8}{10} \times \frac{100}{1} = \frac{800}{10} = 80\%$$

Conversions

Percentage	Decimal	Fraction
75%	0.75	$\frac{3}{4}$
66.66%	$0.6\dot{6}$	$\frac{2}{3}$
50%	0.5	$\frac{1}{2}$
40%	0.4	$\frac{2}{5}$
33.33%	$0.3\dot{3}$	$\frac{1}{3}$
25%	0.25	$\frac{1}{4}$
20%	0.2	$\frac{1}{5}$
12.5%	0.125	$\frac{1}{8}$
10%	0.1	$\frac{1}{10}$
5%	0.05	$\frac{1}{20}$
2%	0.02	$\frac{1}{50}$

Roman numerals

Mathematics – numbers

1	5	10	50	100	500	1000
I	V	X	L	C	D	M

1	I	11	XI	21	XXI
2	II	12	XII	22	XXII
3	III	13	XIII	23	XXIII
4	IV	14	XIV	24	XXIV
5	V	15	XV	25	XXV
6	VI	16	XVI	26	XXVI
7	VII	17	XVII	27	XXVII
8	VIII	18	XVIII	28	XXVIII
9	IX	19	XIX	29	XXIX
10	X	20	XX	30	XXX

35	XXXV	100	C
40	XL	150	CL
45	XLV	200	CC
50	L	300	CCC
55	LV	400	CD
60	LX	500	D
65	LXV	600	DC
70	LXX	700	DCC
75	LXXV	800	DCCC
80	LXXX	900	CM
85	LXXXV	1000	M
90	XC	1500	MD
95	XCV	2000	MM

Patterns occur in numbers in many different ways. Mathematicians have been studying these number patterns for centuries and the discoveries from ancient times have helped us to form our modern view of mathematics.

Simple number patterns such as odd and even numbers are easily identified; however, there are many more complex patterns to be observed.

Some of these are listed below.

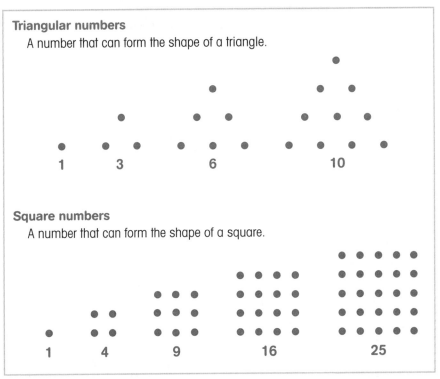

Triangular numbers
A number that can form the shape of a triangle.

1   3   6   10

Square numbers
A number that can form the shape of a square.

1   4   9   16   25

Patterns can be identified in many other ways. Some of these include:

- rectangular numbers
- hexagonal numbers
- pentagonal numbers
- cubic numbers.

Experiment to find what patterns exist in these and other numbers.

Checking strategies

Question your answer

Ask yourself if the answer sounds right. A question you might ask yourself is …

'Is the answer way too big or way too small?'

If you think the answer does not seem right, try looking for patterns.

Odd and even numbers

Odd and even numbers follow a pattern. Once you are aware of the pattern, all you need to do is look at the ones digits of the numbers in the problem and the answer to determine whether the answer is definitely wrong or possibly correct.

Addition	Subtraction	Multiplication
odd + odd = even odd + even = odd even + even = even	odd − odd = even odd − even = odd even − odd = odd even − even = even	odd x odd = odd odd x even = even even x even = even

Estimating

Finding an answer that is close to the exact answer. It is usually found by rounding or by using judgment to make a 'best guess'.

Round down						Round up				
0	1	2	3	4	5	6	7	8	9
10	11	12	13	14	15	16	17	18	19
20	21	22	23	24	25	26	27	28	29
30	31	32	33	34	35	36	37	38	39
40	41	42	43	44	45	46	47	48	49
50	51	52	53	54	55	56	57	58	59
60	61	62	63	64	65	66	67	68	69
70	71	72	73	74	75	76	77	78	79
80	81	82	83	84	85	86	87	88	89
90	91	92	93	94	95	96	97	98	99

When estimating, you should:

1. estimate
2. calculate
3. evaluate (How close was your estimate? Could you improve on your technique?)

Front-end rounding

1. Look at the left-most digit in the number.
2. Consider the place value of the digit.

For example:

$$\begin{array}{r} 3\ 2\ 1\ 5 \\ 6\ 9\ 1\ 0 \\ +\ 4\ 3\ 4\ 2 \\ \hline 3 + 6 + 4 = 13 \end{array}$$

So the estimate would be 13 000.

Rounding

Think about the context of the numbers before rounding.

For example:
When calculating the amount of paint needed to paint a room, it is best to overestimate, so you do not run short.

Mathematics

Repeat the calculation

- carefully, in exactly the same way

- using the inverse operation

- using a different method

Consider the size of the answer

When you read a question, do you ever consider how big the answer will be?

Think about if the answer will be in tens, hundreds, thousands ... or bigger!

There is a pattern that can help alert you to potential errors.

	Number of digits	Answer likely to be in the ...
Addition	1 digit + 1 digit	ones or tens
	2 digits + 1 digit	tens or hundreds
	2 digits + 2 digits	tens or hundreds
	3 digits + 1 digit	hundreds or thousands
	3 digits + 2 digits	hundreds or thousands
	3 digits + 3 digits	hundreds or thousands
Multiplication	1 digit x 1 digit	ones or tens
	2 digits x 1 digit	tens or hundreds
	2 digits x 2 digits	hundreds or thousands
	3 digits x 1 digit	hundreds or thousands
	3 digits x 2 digits	thousands or ten thousands
	3 digits x 3 digits	ten thousands or hundred thousands

Divisibility rules

It is often helpful to know when one number may be divided into another neatly without leaving a remainder.

2	Any even number; e.g. 2, 4, 6, 8 or 0	**6**	Any number divisible by 2 and 3; e.g. 54, 972, 2196
3	Sum of all digits = multiple of 3; e.g. 8652 = 8 + 6 + 5 + 2 = 21 ÷ 3	**9**	Sum of all digits = multiple of 9; e.g. 72 567 = 7 + 2 + 5 + 6 + 7 = 27; 2 + 7 = 9
4	Last two digits divisible by 4; e.g. 23 6<u>32</u>, 45 6<u>56</u>, 13 9<u>88</u>	**10**	Any number ending in 0; e.g. 1<u>0</u>, 20<u>0</u>, 768<u>0</u>, 98 45<u>0</u>
5	Any number ending in 0 or 5; e.g. 2<u>0</u>, 4<u>5</u>, 67<u>0</u>, 984<u>5</u>	**25**	Last two digits divisible by 25; e.g. 64<u>75</u>, 89<u>50</u>

Mathematics – money

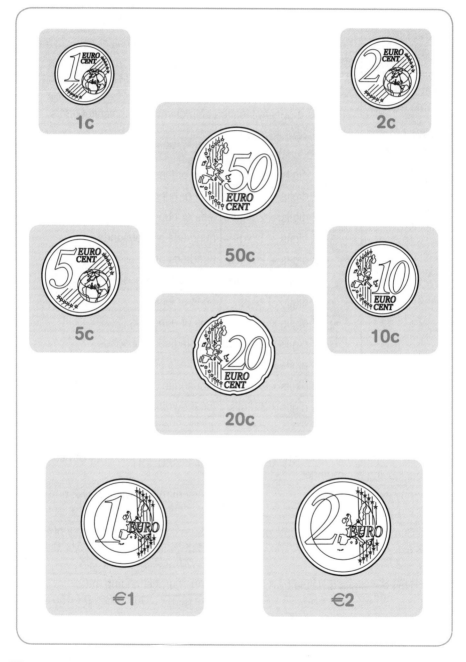

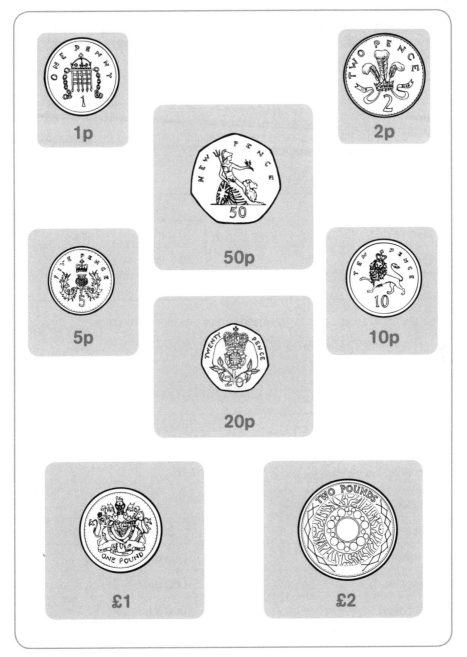

1p

2p

50p

5p

10p

20p

£1

£2

Length & mass

Mathematics – measurement

The two main systems of general measurement used throughout the world are the metric and the imperial. The metric system is used in the majority of countries.

The metric system is a decimal system of measure.

Length

The following are the units used to measure length. (Note the space between the symbol and the number.)

Unit	Symbol
millimetre(s)	mm
centimetre(s)	cm
metre(s)	m
kilometre(s)	km

Equivalent measures	
10 mm	1 cm
100 cm	1 m
1000 m	1 km

Measurements should always be written in only one form of measure.

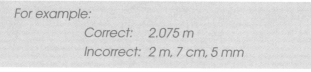

For example:
Correct: *2.075 m*
Incorrect: *2 m, 7 cm, 5 mm*

Mass

The following are the units used to measure mass. (Note the space between the symbol and the number.)

Unit	Symbol
milligram(s)	mg
gram(s)	g
kilogram(s)	kg
tonne(s)	t

Equivalent measures	
1000 mg	1 g
1000 g	1 kg
1000 kg	1 t

Area

The following are the units used to measure area.

Unit	Symbol
square millimetre(s)	mm^2
square centimetre(s)	cm^2
square metre(s)	m^2
hectare(s)	ha
kilometre(s)	km^2

1 cm^2 1 mm^2

1 m^2

1 m^2

1 m^2

Equivalent measures	
100 mm^2	1 cm^2
10 000 cm^2	1 m^2
10 000 m^2	1 ha
100 ha	1 km^2

These can be spoken as 'square centimetre', 'square metre' or 'square kilometre'.

(Note the space between the symbol and the number.)

Capacity

The amount of space in the 'interior' of an object is measured in cubic units.

The following are the units used to measure capacity.

Unit	Symbol
millilitre(s)	mL
litre(s)	L
kilolitre(s)	kL

Equivalent measures	
1000 mL	1 L
1000 L	1 kL

(Note the space between the symbol and the number.)

Volume

The amount of space taken up by an object.
The following are the units used to measure volume.

Unit	Symbol
cubic millimetre(s)	mm³
cubic centimetre(s)	cm³
cubic metre(s)	m³

Equivalent measures	
1000 mm³	1 cm³
1 000 000 cm³	1 m³

(Note the space between the symbol and the number.)

The three dimensions of a cubic measure are:
- length
- height
- width

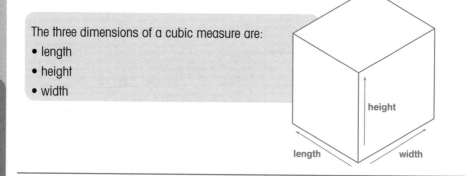

Temperature

Temperature is measured in either Celsius or Fahrenheit. Celsius measures are recorded in this way. (Note the space between the symbol and the number.):

24 °C

Symbol	Unit
°C	degrees Celsius
°F	degrees Fahrenheit
K	Kelvin

Two significant measures in Celsius measurement are the freezing and boiling points of water.

Freezing point: 0 °C
Boiling point: 100 °C

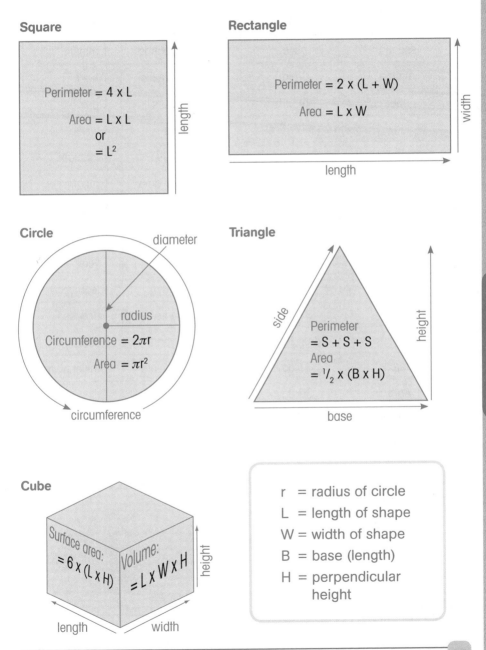

Square

Perimeter = 4 x L

Area = L x L
or
= L²

length

Rectangle

Perimeter = 2 x (L + W)

Area = L x W

width

length

Circle

diameter

radius

Circumference = 2πr

Area = πr²

circumference

Triangle

side

Perimeter
= S + S + S
Area
= ¹/₂ x (B x H)

height

base

Cube

Surface area:
= 6 x (L x H)

Volume:
= L x W x H

height

length   *width*

r = radius of circle
L = length of shape
W = width of shape
B = base (length)
H = perpendicular
     height

Time

Mathematics – measurement

The measurement of time is not a decimal system of measure.

Unit	Abbreviation
second	sec.
minute	min.
hour	hr or h.
day	d
month	m.
year	yr or y.
century	C
millennium	M

Equivalent measures	
60 seconds	1 minute
60 minutes	1 hour
24 hours	1 day
7 days	1 week
14 days	1 fortnight
28–31 days	1 month
52 weeks	1 year
12 months	1 year
365 days	1 year
366 days	1 leap year
10 years	1 decade
100 years	1 century
1000 years	1 millennium

Months of the year	
January	31 days
February	28 or 29 days
March	31 days
April	30 days
May	31 days
June	30 days
July	31 days
August	31 days
September	30 days
October	31 days
November	30 days
December	31 days

Seasons
Spring
Summer
Autumn
Winter

Time can be a moment, hour, day or year as shown on a clock or calendar.
Time can be shown in digital form, analogue or 24-hour time.

Conversion

24-hour time	Analogue time
0000	midnight
0100	1.00
0200	2.00
0300	3.00
0400	4.00
0500	5.00
0600	6.00
0700	7.00
0800	8.00
0900	9.00
1000	10.00
1100	11.00
1200	midday
1300	1.00
1400	2.00
1500	3.00
1600	4.00
1700	5.00
1800	6.00
1900	7.00
2000	8.00
2100	9.00
2200	10.00
2300	11.00

Analogue clocks

An analogue clock shows the time by continuously moving two hands. It usually has an hour hand and a minute hand.

Right Time Clock Co.

am and pm

The day is divided into:

* am
  before noon (ante meridiem)

* pm
  after noon (post meridiem).

Time can also be a measure or measurable period during which something takes place.

In some sporting activities, times are measured to one-hundredths of a second using a stopwatch.

Line

Made up of an infinite set of points extending in both directions.

Ray

Made up of an infinite set of points emanating from a point and going in one direction.

Line segment

A line with two end points.

Diagonal

A straight line joining two non-adjacent vertices of a polygon.

Horizontal

A line parallel to the horizon.

Vertical

A line which is at right angles to a horizontal line.

Perpendicular

Lines at right angles to another line or plane.

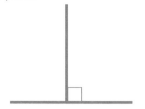

Parallel

Lines that are always the same distance apart and have no common points.

There are different types of angles.

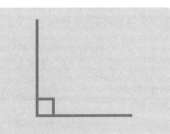

Straight angle

An angle of exactly 180°.

Right angle

An angle of exactly 90°.

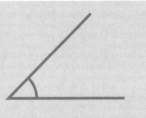

Acute angle

An angle less than 90°.

Reflex angle

An angle between 180° and 360°.

An angle is the space formed by two intersecting lines or surfaces near where they meet.

Angles are measured in degrees. The symbol for degree is °.

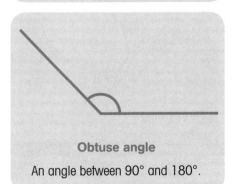

Obtuse angle

An angle between 90° and 180°.

A degree is a unit of angular measure. There are 360° in one complete rotation. A protractor is a tool used to measure the size of an angle.

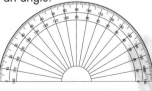

Plane figures

Mathematics – shape and space

Plane figures are those shapes that occupy a space on a plane. They may have curved or straight sides.

Plane figures with straight sides are called polygons.

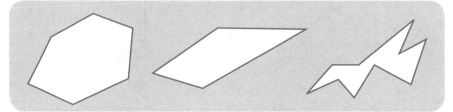

Those polygons with sides of equal length are called regular polygons.

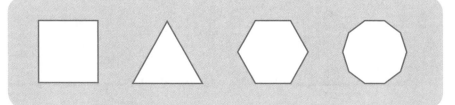

Other plane shapes include circles and ellipses.

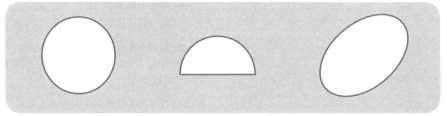

Parts of a circle include the following:

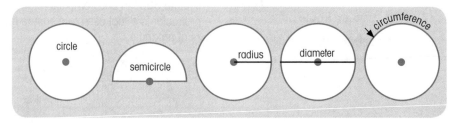

Mathematics – shape and space

Sides/ Angles	Name	Shape
3	triangle	
4	square	
4	rectangle	
5	pentagon	
6	hexagon	
7	heptagon	
8	octagon	
9	nonagon	
10	decagon	

Solid figures

Mathematics – shape and space

Solid figures are also called three-dimensional figures.

A solid figure has length, width and height.

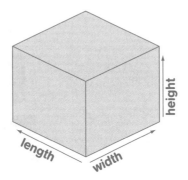

Parts of a solid figure include the following:

Faces: the surface area(s) of a three-dimensional figure.

Edges: the intersection(s) of two faces of a three-dimensional figure.

Vertices: the intersection(s) of two or more edges of a three-dimensional figure.

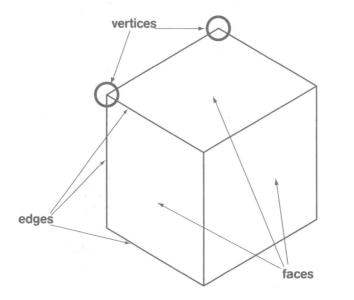

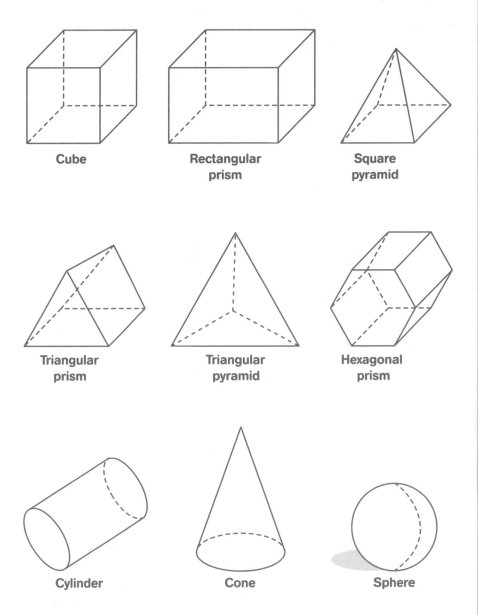

Cube

Rectangular prism

Square pyramid

Triangular prism

Triangular pyramid

Hexagonal prism

Cylinder

Cone

Sphere

Mathematics – shape and space

Coordinates

A point on a grid can be referenced using an 'ordered pair' of numbers (or numbers and letters). These are called the coordinates of the point.

The horizontal axis is always read or written before the vertical axis.

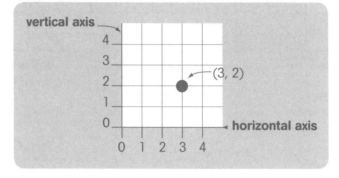

Transformations

A transformation is a movement that doesn't change the size or shape of a figure.

These movements are:

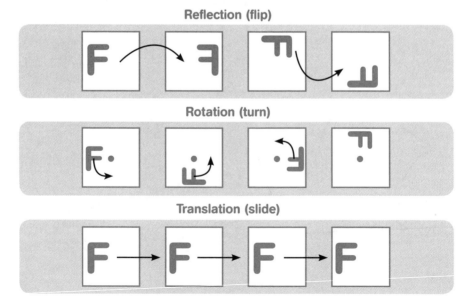

Information is often recorded in pictorial form. This can be done in many different ways depending on how we need the information to be presented.

Bar graph

A graph which represents information regarding frequency of outcomes using bar lengths.

The graph has a vertical and horizontal axis. The bars may be vertical or horizontal.

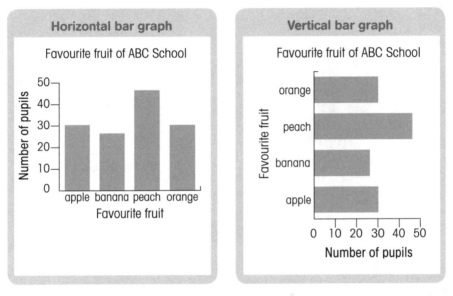

Horizontal bar graph

Favourite fruit of ABC School

Vertical bar graph

Favourite fruit of ABC School

Line graph

A graph which has a vertical and horizontal axis and is formed by joining points with straight lines or a curve to represent data.

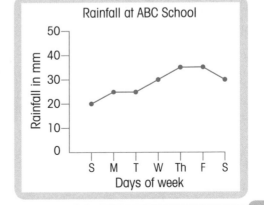

Rainfall at ABC School

Pictogram

A graph in which data is represented by pictures. One picture could represent one unit or many.

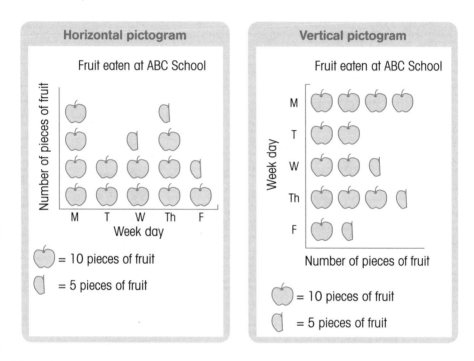

Horizontal pictogram

Fruit eaten at ABC School

Number of pieces of fruit / Week day — M T W Th F

= 10 pieces of fruit

= 5 pieces of fruit

Vertical pictogram

Fruit eaten at ABC School

Week day — M T W Th F / Number of pieces of fruit

= 10 pieces of fruit

= 5 pieces of fruit

Pie chart

A graph in which portions of a circle are used to show a total divided into parts.

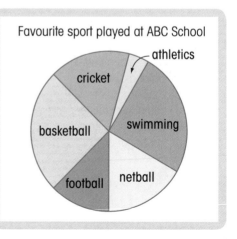

Favourite sport played at ABC School

athletics
cricket
swimming
basketball
netball
football

Some data is best displayed in a diagram. There are many different types of diagrams.

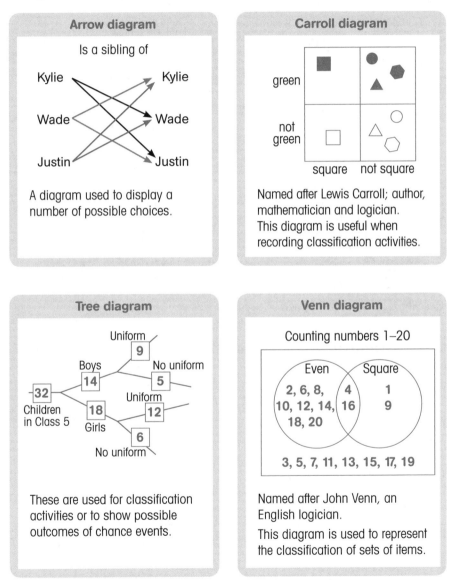

Arrow diagram

Is a sibling of

A diagram used to display a number of possible choices.

Carroll diagram

Named after Lewis Carroll; author, mathematician and logician. This diagram is useful when recording classification activities.

Tree diagram

These are used for classification activities or to show possible outcomes of chance events.

Venn diagram

Named after John Venn, an English logician.

This diagram is used to represent the classification of sets of items.

Recording data & statistics

Mathematics – chance and data

Recording data

<table>
<tr><th colspan="5">Tables</th></tr>
<tr><th colspan="5">Number of children in each team</th></tr>
<tr><td></td><td>Blue</td><td>Red</td><td>Green</td><td>Gold</td></tr>
<tr><td>Boys</td><td>46</td><td>43</td><td>49</td><td>32</td></tr>
<tr><td>Girls</td><td>40</td><td>50</td><td>35</td><td>49</td></tr>
<tr><td>Total</td><td>86</td><td>93</td><td>84</td><td>81</td></tr>
</table>

These are used to organise data for a particular purpose.

Tallies

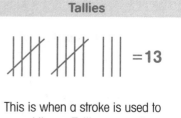 =13

This is when a stroke is used to record items. Tallies generally use a diagonal stroke on the fifth item.

Statistics

Data can be collected from a set group of people or from a 'random sample'. A 'random sample' is when every person has the same chance of being included in the sample.

For example,
I have randomly collected the test scores of 7 pupils in the class.
11   14   12   16   17   16   20

Once the data is collected it can be used to calculate:

Range (of a distribution)

The difference between the greatest and least values in a set of data.

For example:
Greatest value = 20, least value = 11.
Therefore the range is 20 – 11 = 9.
The range is 9.

Mode (frequency)

The measurement or observation that occurs most often; the item with the highest frequency.

For example:
The test score which occurs most frequently is 16.
The mode is 16.

Mean (average)

The mean of a set of numbers is a single number used to represent the set. It is calculated by dividing the sum of the numbers by the number in the sample.

For example:
11 + 14 + 12 + 16 + 17 + 16 + 20 = 106
106 ÷ 7 (pupils) = 15.14
The mean is 15.14.

Median

The middle measurement, or score, when items are arranged in order of size. Where there is no middle score, a mean of the two central scores is taken.

For example:
11, 12, 14, 16, 16, 17, 20
The median is 16.

Essential facts and tables

alliteration

the use of the same sound at the beginning of a series of words; e.g. ten terrific teddies

analogy

a likeness between things; e.g. analogy between a heart and a pump

assonance

using the same vowel sounds in words which follow each other or are close together

ballad

a narrative poem often including a lot of action

cinquain

a poem of five lines
1st line – is a noun
2nd line – is two adjectives describing the noun in line one.
3rd line – three words describing the noun in an active form.
4th line – four words telling what the noun does.
5th line – repeats the first line

colloquialism

colloquialisms are expressions used in common conversation. They usually sum up a situation and are particular to a certain area; e.g. hit the nail on the head – to be right; g'day (Australian) – hello.

fable

a short tale that teaches a moral and often portrays animals as characters

fairytale

stories told of amazing happenings. Characters often have special powers and stories relate to times in the past.

folktale

traditional stories, poems and songs passed down from generation to generation

haiku

a Japanese verse that succinctly describes an aspect of nature in 17 syllables; it has three lines
line 1 – 5 syllables; line 2 – 7 syllables; line 3 – 5 syllables

legend

folkstories of great significance handed down through generations

limerick

a five-line nonsense poem where the first, second and fifth lines rhyme, while the third and fourth lines rhyme

metaphor

a term or phrase is used to compare with something which it is not literally suitable; e.g. a mighty oak tree is our father

myth

an ancient story made up to explain the existence of a thing or event

onomatopoeia

the formation of a word by imitating a sound associated; e.g. hiccup

personification

to describe non-human things in a human way

proverb

a group of words that present a wise thought; e.g. many hands make light work

simile

comparison between two objects using the words 'like' or 'as'; e.g. as cold as ice

tautology

unnecessary repetition of a message in a sentence using different words; e.g. He struggled upstream with great effort.

Parts of speech

English

adjective

a word used to describe a noun or a pronoun. It can:

- tell us more information; e.g. The tall, blue vase was used to decorate the table.
- tell how much or how many; e.g. There were sixteen boys on the bus.
- tell us who owns something; e.g. That is my notebook.
- compare two or more nouns; e.g. Elephants are larger than lions.
- be a proper adjective; e.g. The Australian people are very friendly.

adverb

a word used to describe the verb. It can:

- tell us when; e.g. The class finished early on Friday.
- tell us how; e.g. The boy quickly ran through the field.
- tell us where; e.g. The children ran outside in the sunshine.
- compare the way in which actions are done; e.g. Connor ran faster than Noah.

conjunction

a word used to join two single words, two phrases or two clauses; e.g. It was a bright sunny day because it was the middle of August.

interjection

a word or word group to show emotion. It is often followed by an exclamation mark; e.g. Congratulations on winning the game!

noun

a word used to name a person, place, thing, feeling or an idea. It can be:

- a common noun; e.g. child, table
- a proper noun; e.g. Anna, January
- a collective noun; e.g. bunch of bananas, litter of pups
- an abstract noun; e.g. love, fear, happiness

preposition

a word that shows the connection between a noun and other words in a sentence; e.g. The boy walked beside the road.

pronoun

a word used in the place of a noun; e.g. it, him, her, I, them

verb

a word used to show action or a state of being. Every sentence should have a verb. There are:

- action verbs; e.g. I love eating chocolate.
- helping verbs; e.g. My mum was smiling at my dad.

Verbs can show the time of the action (the tense).

- present tense; e.g. The baby is crying.
- past tense; e.g. The baby was crying.
- future tense; e.g. The baby will cry.

sentence

a word or a sequence of words which begins with a capital letter, ends with a punctuation mark and usually has a 'subject' (noun or pronoun) and a 'predicate' (verb or adverb). A sentence forms a complete thought and should make sense no matter how few or how many words it contains.

There are different types of sentences.

- Declarative sentences usually make a statement or give information; e.g. We are going on holiday tomorrow.
- Imperative sentences give a command or instruction; e.g. Please close the fridge door when you have finished.
- Interrogative sentences ask a question and end with a question mark; e.g. Where have you been?
- Exclamatory sentences express a strong emotion or feeling and usually end with an exclamation mark; e.g. Watch out!

English

apostrophe

- of ownership/possession: is where an apostrophe is used to replace 'of'; e.g. The clothes of the boy: The boy's clothes.
- used to show when a letter or letters have been omitted; e.g. did not – didn't.

brackets (parentheses)

used to incorporate additional information into a sentence; e.g. The two boys (who were brothers) were very polite children.

capital letter

used at the beginning of a sentence, as the first letter in a proper noun, in some abbreviations and for the word 'I'.

colon

used to mark off the main part of the sentence and to introduce a list or series of topics or ideas; e.g. For the football match tomorrow bring: a raincoat, a hat, biscuits, coffee and sandwiches.

comma

- marks a short pause in reading to help give a sentence sense; e.g. The team struggled, even though they had won previously.
- divides items in a sentence; e.g. James invited John, Mary, Gary and Julia to his birthday.
- separates direct speech from the sentence.
- used to insert information within a sentence; e.g. The wall, which was falling down, was roped off from the children.

dash

used to indicate a break in a sentence; e.g. I'm coming—don't wait—straightaway.

ellipsis

marks where there is a break in thought or where words are left out; e.g. Colby muttered 'Well … um … er … I didn't mean to break the window'.

exclamation mark

used at the end of a sentence to show strong feelings or emotion; e.g. Stop, thief!

full stop

used to show the end of a sentence. Also used in some abbreviations.

hyphen

used to show how words are joined to create meaning; e.g. soon-to-be bride

question mark

used at the end of a sentence to indicate a question is being asked

quotation marks

- used to show where direct speech is being used
- may also used to indicate names of books, films, poems etc.

semicolon

used to separate parts of a sentence where there is a more distinct break than one designated by a comma

'	apostrophe
( )	brackets (parentheses)
:	colon
,	comma
–	dash
...	ellipsis
!	exclamation mark
.	full stop
-	hyphen
?	question mark
' '	quotation marks (single)
" "	quotation marks (double)
;	semicolon

Constructing text

English

1

Decide:
- what you are going to write about (purpose)
- who you are going to write for (audience)

2

Choose:
- a working title (This may change at the end.)
- the form of text which best suits your purpose. Use the appropriate framework.

3

Generate:
- ideas and thoughts for your writing (These may be events, feelings, information, facts and so on.)
- notes and facts that will help you in your writing

4

Organise:
- your ideas, thoughts and notes under the correct headings of your framework (You may find it easier to present your ideas, thoughts and notes as a graphic organiser.)

5

Write:
- a draft paragraph for each heading of your framework. You will be able to use your ideas, thoughts and notes as a base for your writing.

6

Edit:
- your work by following a proofreading and editing checklist
- your work by sharing the draft with others. Read it aloud and make corrections where necessary.

7

Present:
- your polished piece of writing to the audience

Proofreading & editing checklist

Text
Have I:
- chosen the correct framework for my purpose? ☐
- used suitable language? ☐
- checked that my information is accurate? ☐
- included enough detail? ☐
- made my writing interesting? ☐

Punctuation
Consider the use of:
- full stops, question and exclamation marks ☐
- capital letters ☐
- commas, colons, semicolons ☐
- apostrophes ☐
- quotation marks ☐
- hyphens, dashes and brackets ☐

Spelling
Carefully check:
- any spelling of unknown words ☐
- names of people, places, animals and technical terms ☐

Grammar
Be sure to include:
- a variety of different verbs ☐
- interesting adverbs ☐
- the correct noun/verb agreement ☐
- pronouns that correctly match the noun ☐
- interesting adjectives ☐
- a variety of suitable conjunctions and prepositions ☐
- the correct tense ☐
- varied sentence lengths and patterns ☐

Spelling rules

English

1. 'i' before 'e' except after 'c' with the sound of 'eeee' (exception 'seize').

   e.g. brief; receive

2. Short 'a', 'e', 'i', 'o', 'u', are followed by 'ck' (in one-syllable words).

   e.g. back; pluck

3. When 'c' or 'g' are followed by 'a', 'o' or 'u', they have a hard sound.

   e.g. colour; gold

   When 'c' or 'g' are followed by 'e' or 'i' they usually have a soft sound.

   e.g. cinema; germ

   When 'c' is followed by 'y' it also has a soft sound.

   e.g. cycle

4. For the hard 'k' sound; 'k' goes in front of 'e' and 'i'; 'c' goes in front of 'a', 'o' and 'u'.

   e.g. kelp, kick; cat, cot, cut

5. 'k', 'g' and 'p' are silent at the beginning of a word if followed by a consonant (usually 'n').

   e.g. knee; gnaw; pneumonia

6. The consonants 'f', 'l' and 's' are doubled at the end of most words of one syllable.

   e.g. ball; cliff; kiss

7. Most words of two or more syllables ending in 'l' have only one final 'l'.

   e.g. parallel; initial

8. When a word ends in an 'e' the 'e' is usually dropped when a suffix beginning with a vowel is added.

   e.g. bake + ing = baking

9. When a word ends in an 'e' the 'e' is usually kept when a suffix beginning with a consonant is added. Usually the 'e' is dropped when adding a suffix beginning with a vowel.

   e.g. price + less = priceless;
   love + able = lovable

10. When adding 'y' to a word ending in 'e', drop the 'e' before adding 'y'.

    e.g. ease–easy; noise–noisy

11. Change the final 'y' to 'i' before adding any suffix, except with '–ing' or when 'y' follows a vowel.

    e.g. carry–carried; carry–carrying

12. Words ending in '–ce' and '–ge' drop the '–e' when '–ing' is added but retain the '–e' when '–able' and '–ous' are added.

    e.g. notice; noticing; noticeable

13. A short vowel sound should always be followed by two consonants when adding '–y', '–ed', '–ing' or '–er'.

    e.g. run–running; jump–jumper

14. Words which end in a single consonant preceded by a short, accented vowel sound, double the consonant when a suffix beginning with a vowel is added.

    e.g. bat; batted; batting; batter

15. Words which end in a single consonant preceded by a long vowel do not double the consonant when a suffix beginning with a vowel is added.

e.g. beat; beaten; beating; beater

16. Adjectives ending in '–le' after a consonant form adverbs by dropping the 'e' and adding a 'y'.

e.g. gentle; gentl–y

17. When the suffix '–ice' or '–ise' is written after a word, '–ice' is used for nouns; 'is' is a verb and, therefore, '–ise' is used for verbs.

e.g. (verbs) exercise; practise (nouns) notice; practice

18. Words ending in a single consonant other than 'l', but not accented on the last syllable, do not double the consonant when a suffix is added.

e.g. gallop; galloper; galloping

19. When the words 'all', 'full', 'fill' and 'till' are used as suffixes and prefixes, one 'l' is dropped.

e.g. already; fulfil

20. The prefixes 'dis–' and 'mis–' never drop their 's', even when added to a word beginning with 's'.

e.g. dis–ability; dis–satisfied

21. Making words plural:
  (a) Just add '–s' to most nouns and words ending in '–ful'.

  e.g. biscuits; handfuls

  (b) Add '–es' to nouns ending in '–ch', '–sh', '–o', '–s', '–x' or '–z'.

  e.g. classes; buzzes; foxes; potatoes; arches; leashes

  Note: zeros or zeroes, mosquitoes or mosquitos

  (c) Change 'f' to 'v' for words ending in '–f' or '–fe'.

  e.g. calf–calves; wife–wives

  (d) Some words change their vowels.

  e.g. man–men; tooth–teeth

22. Making words past tense:
  (a) Just add '–ed' or '–d'.

  e.g. trace–traced; talk–talked

  (b) Verbs with a short vowel sound followed by a short consonant sound have the final letter doubled.

  e.g. fit–fitted; trap–trapped

  (c) Some words use '–t'.

  e.g. weep–wept; sleep–slept

  (d) Some words change their spelling.

  e.g. rise–rose; run–ran

Prefixes

English

A prefix is a word part added to the beginning of a word.
It can change the meaning of that word.

Prefix	Meaning	Example
a	on, at, up, out, to	ashore, asleep, ahead
a–, ab–	away from	absent
after–	following	afternoon, afterthought
anti–	against	antiseptic, anti-war
auto–	self	autobiography
bi–	two	bicycle, biped
circum–	around	circumference
co–, com–, con–	together, with	companion, conflict
contra	against	contrary, contradiction
de–	down, away	descend
dif–, dis–	apart from, not	different, disagree
down–	downwards	downfall, downpour
e–, ex–, out–	out, or out of	export, emigrate, outside
en–	make	enclose, enrich
extra–	outside, beyond	extraordinary
fore–	in front, before	forehand, forehead
il–	not	illegal, illegible
im–, in–	not	impossible, independent
im–, in–	into, in	inspect, inland, immerse
inter–	between, among	interact, intersection
ir–	not	irregular, irresponsible
mid–	middle	midday, midnight
mis–	wrong	misfortune, misunderstand
non–	not	nonsense
over–	over, beyond, too much	overgrown, overcharge
post–	after	post meridiem (pm), postscript
pre–	before	precaution, prefix
pro–	for	proceed, produce
re–	again, back	redo, replace, return
sub–	under	submarine, subsonic
super–	over	supermarket, supersonic
tele–	far away	telegram, television
trans–	across	transport, transcontinental
un–	not	unfair, uneven, unselfish
under–	under, beneath	underline, underneath

A suffix is a word part added to the end of a word. Sometimes when suffixes are added, the spelling of the base word changes; e.g. happy–happily.

Suffix	Meaning	Example
–able	tending to, able to	enjoyable, movable
–age	state of being, place of, result of	wastage, shrinkage, orphanage
–al	relating to, belonging to	electrical, residential
–an	pertaining to	comedian, Australian
–ance, –ence	state of being	excellence, disappearance
–ary, ery	that which, place where	bakery, parliamentary
–ate	to make	donate, separate
–en	having nature of	fallen, broken, golden
–en	to make or become	widen, whiten, flatten
–er	one who, that which	worker, teacher
–er	more (in degree)	taller, faster, smarter
–ese	belonging to	Chinese, Japanese
–est	most (in degree)	cleanest, loudest
–ful	full of	cheerful, helpful
–fy	make or form into	identify, notify
–hood	state, character, nature	childhood, neighbourhood
–ible	tending to, able to	sensible, possible
–ic	like, belonging to	athletic, artistic
–ion	act, process, state	action, education
–ish	like	whitish, foolish, childish
–ist	one who	artist, journalist
–ive	having nature of	active, creative
–less	without	worthless, helpless
–ling	small, little	duckling, gosling
–ly	in the manner of	happily, sadly, quietly
–ment	resulting state, action	treatment, employment
–most	most (in degree)	topmost, northernmost
–ness	quality or state of being	weakness, sickness
–or	person who	actor, director
–ous	state or condition	nervous, dangerous
–ship	state of being	hardship, friendship
–ure	act, process	pleasure, adventure

Root words

Root words are words from another language which have been used to form words in the English language.

Root	Meaning
acro–	top
aero	air
alter	other
alto	high
amor	love
amphi–	on all sides
–androus	male
anima	breath, life
aniso–	unlike
anthropo–	human
apia	bee
aqua	water
audio–	hear
auto–	self
avi–	bird
baro–	weight
bene–	good, well
benz–	derivative
bi	twice, two
biblio–	book
bio–	life
brevi–	short
capere	to take hold
caput	head
cardio–	heart
centum	hundred
–chrome	colour
chrono–	time
–cide	killer
circum–	around
civis	citizen
–claudere	shut, close
cor	heart
cosmeo	world
counter–	against

Root	Meaning
cranium–	skull
credo	I believe
crypto–	hidden
crystallo–	crystal
cursus	running
cycl–	cycle
cyst–	cyst
–cyte	cell
cyto–	cell
deca–	ten
demo–	people
demon–	demon
denti–	tooth
–derm	skin
ducere	to lead
duo–	two
dys–	bad
endo–	within, inside
entero–	intestine
equi	equal
ethno–	race, tribe
factor	do
fertilis	to make fruitful
finis	end
fluor	flow
gastro–	stomach
geo–	earth
–gerous	producing
–gram	letter, writing
–graph	write
gyn–	woman
gyro–	circle
hetero–	other
holo–	whole
homo–	same

Root	Meaning
ideo–	idea
manus	hand
mille	thousand
mini–	small
minuere	to lessen
mittere	to send
mono–	one, alone
–morph	form
mors	death
movere	move
multi–	many
my–	muscle
myc–	fungus
myth–	myth
myx–	slimy
natus	born
navis	ship
nector	dead
neo–	new
nepho–	cloud
nephro–	kidney
nocti–	night
novem	nine
octa	eight
omni–	all
ortho–	straight, right
paed–	child
pan–	all
patho–	suffering
pedis	foot
pendere	hang
penta–	five
–phasia	disordered speech
phen	used in chemical terms
–philia	lover of
phlebo–	vein
–phobia	fear
phon–	sound, voice

Root	Meaning
–phorous	bearing, having
phosp–	phosphorus
photo–	light
physio–	physical
phyto–	plant
–plasty	formation
poly–	many
portare	carry, bear
prima	first
project	throw
proto–	first
pseudo–	false
psych–	mind
ptero–	wing
pyo–	pus
quadri–	four
quinque–	five
recti–	set upright
scrib	write
–sect	cut
septum	seven
sex–	six
Sino–	Chinese
spectro–	look
–spermal	sperm
–sphere	sphere
spiro–	spiral
–stat	stationary
statua	statue
tele–	afar, end
terra	earth
tetra	four
tractum	trace
tri–	three
uni–	one
video	see
vox	voice

Homonyms

Homophones are a type of homonym. Homophones are words that sound the same whether spelt the same or not.

allowed/aloud	gait/gate	road/rode/rowed
altar/alter	guessed/guest	rote/wrote
aren't/aunt	hair/hare	sail/sale
ate/eight	hail/hale	sauce/source
bare/bear	hear/here	saw/sore
berry/bury	heard/herd	scene/seen
berth/birth	hoarse/horse	sea/see
blew/blue	hole/whole	seam/seem
board/bored	hour/our	sew/so/sow
boarder/border	idle/idol	shore/sure
bough/bow	key/quay	sight/site
boy/buoy	knead/need	son/sun
brake/break	knew/new	stair/stare
buy/by/bye	knight/night	stake/steak
caught/court	know/no	stationary/stationery
cent/scent/sent	lead/led	steal/steel
ceiling/sealing	load/lode	storey/story
cereal/serial	made/maid	straight/strait
cheap/cheep	main/mane	tail/tale
check/cheque	mare/mayor	team/teem
chews/choose	meat/meet/mete	their/there/they're
coarse/course	medal/meddle	threw/through
complement/compliment	muscle/mussel	throne/thrown
council/counsel	none/nun	to/too/two
currant/current	one/won	vain/vane/vein
die/dye	paced/paste	waist/waste
discreet/discrete	pair/pare/pear	wait/weight
faint/feint	paw/poor/pore/pour	wear/where
fair/fare	peace/piece	weak/week
fate/fete	plain/plane	weal/wheel
feat/feet	practice/practise	weather/wether/whether
flaw/floor	rap/wrap	which/witch
foul/fowl	right/rite/write	wood/would

Other homonyms are called homographs. Homographs are spelt the same, sound the same, but have a different origin and meaning.

For example:
bear and bear, rock and rock, chip and chip, nail and nail.

Synonyms

Words that are similar in meaning.

Word	Synonym
walk	stroll
run	sprint, jog
jump	leap
gift	present
happen	occur
squirm	wriggle
stopped	ceased
found	discovered
looked	peered
dragged	hauled
soaked	drenched
said	exclaimed
lived	dwelt
cried	wept

Antonyms

Words that are opposite in meaning.

Word	Antonym
happy	miserable
moist	dry
honest	deceitful
frequently	rarely
flexible	stiff
energetic	lazy
wonderful	terrible
build	destroy
common	rare
well-mannered	rude
fancy	plain
relaxed	tense
sharp	blunt
peaceful	noisy

Record some of your own:

Record some of your own:

Collective nouns

English

anthology	of	stories
archipelago	of	islands
armada, fleet	of	ships
army	of	soldiers
assembly	of	people
bale	of	wool, hay
band	of	musicians
bench	of	magistrates
board	of	directors
bouquet	of	flowers
brood	of	chicks
bunch	of	flowers, bananas
chain	of	mountains
chest	of	drawers
choir	of	singers
class	of	students, pupils
cluster	of	gemstones
collection	of	stamps, coins
company	of	actors
congregation	of	worshippers
constellation	of	stars
crew	of	sailors
flight	of	planes
flock	of	birds, sheep
flotilla	of	ships
forest	of	trees
gaggle	of	geese
galaxy	of	stars
grove	of	trees
hand	of	bananas
herd	of	cattle

hive	of	bees
host	of	angels
library	of	books
litter	of	pups, pigs
mob	of	kangaroos, cattle
nest	of	eggs
orchard	of	fruit trees
orchestra	of	musicians
pack	of	wolves
plague	of	insects, locusts
pride	of	lions
punnet	of	strawberries
range	of	mountains
regiment	of	soldiers
rope, string	of	pearls
school	of	fish
sheaf	of	arrows, wheat
shoal	of	fish
skein	of	wool, geese (when in flight)
string	of	horses, beads
suit	of	clothes
suite	of	furniture
swarm	of	insects, bees
team	of	sportspeople
tribe	of	people
troop	of	monkeys, scouts
troupe	of	performers, actors
vineyard	of	grapes

Contractions are found in both written and spoken English. They are a shortened way of writing or speaking two words.

An apostrophe (') of contraction is used to show where a letter or letters are left out when joining two words to make a contraction.

am

I am	I'm

not

was not	wasn't
does not	doesn't
are not	aren't
had not	hadn't
can not	can't
will not	won't
would not	wouldn't
should not	shouldn't
did not	didn't
do not	don't
shall not	shan't
dare not	daren't
is not	isn't
have not	haven't
were not	weren't
could not	couldn't

is

it is	it's
there is	there's
he is	he's
where is	where's
who is	who's
she is	she's

will

we will	we'll
she will	she'll
I will	I'll
you will	you'll
they will	they'll
who will	who'll

would

we would	we'd
I would	I'd
there would	there'd
you would	you'd
he would	he'd

have

we have	we've
you have	you've
they have	they've

are

we are	we're
you are	you're
they are	they're

Shortened forms & acronyms

English

A	
abb. or abbrev.	abbreviation
AD	in the year of our Lord (Anno Domini)
AGM	Annual General Meeting
AIDS	acquired immune deficiency syndrome
a.m.	before noon (ante meridiem)
anon.	anonymous
ans.	answer
approx.	approximately
a.s.a.p.	as soon as possible
Aug.	August
Aust.	Australia
Ave	Avenue

B	
BBC	British Broadcasting Corporation
BBQ	barbecue
BC	Before Christ
bros	brothers
BYO	bring your own
BST	British Summer Time

C	
C	Cape; Celsius; Centigrade; century, carbon
c/o	care of
c.	cent; century; chapter, circa
Capt	Captain
CD	compact disc
Co.	company, county
COD	cash on delivery (also C.O.D.)
Corp.	corporation, Corporal
Cres.	Crescent
CV	Curriculum Vitae

D	
dec.	deceased
Dec.	December
DOB	date of birth
doz.	dozen
Dr	Doctor; Drive

E	
E	east; eastern
e.g.	for example (exempli gratia)
equiv.	equivalent
ESP	extrasensory perception
Esq.	Esquire
est.	established
etc.	and so on (et cetera)
E.U.	European Union

F	
F	Fahrenheit
FA	Football Association
Feb.	February
fem.	feminine
Fr	Father
Fri.	Friday
fwd	forward
f.w.d.	four-wheel drive/front-wheel drive

G	
GB	Great Britain
GM	General Manager/General Motors
GMT	Greenwich Mean Time
Govt	Government
GPO	General Post Office

H	
hdqrs	headquarters
HM	Her (or His) Majesty
HMS	Her (or His) Majesty's Ship
HO	Head Office
Hon.	honorary; honourable
HQ	Headquarters
HRS	Her (or His) Royal Highness

I	
ICT	Information Communication Technology
ID	identification
i.e.	that is (id est)
IOU	I owe you
Ire	Ireland
ISBN	International Standard Book Number

J	
Jan.	January
jnr	junior
Jp	Justice of the Peace
Jul.	July
Jun.	June

K	
km	kilometre
km/h	kilometres per hour

L	
L	learner (driver)
lat.	latitude
l.b.w.	leg before wicket
Ltd.	Limited

M	
Mar.	March

masc.	masculine
maths	mathematics
Messrs	plural of Mr
mill.	million/s
min.	minimum
misc.	miscellaneous
Mon.	Monday
MP	Member of Parliament; Military Police
Mr	Mister
Mrs	Mistress (missus)
Mt	mount; mountain
N	
N	north
n/a	not applicable
NB	note well (nota bene)
NE	north-east
No.	number
NSPCC	National Society for the Prevention of Cruelty to Children
NW	north-west
O	
O.A.P.	Old age pensioner
Oct.	October
OHMS	On Her/His Majesty's Service
o.n.o.	or nearest offer
opp.	opposite
P	
p.a.	per annum (yearly)
p + p	postage and packaging
p.c.	per cent
P.E.	physical education
Pk	Park
Pl.	Place
P.M.	Prime Minister
p.m.	afternoon (post meridiem)
PO	Post Office
POW	prisoner of war
PR	public relations
Prof.	Professor
PS	postscript
P.T.O.	please turn over/power take off
Pty	proprietary
p.w.	per week
Q	
Q	Queen
qtr	quarter

R	
r.	radius
R.A.F	Royal Air Force
R.C.	Roman Catholic
Rd	Road
R.E.	Religious Education
recd	received
Rev.	Reverend
r.p.m.	revolutions per minute
RSPCA	Royal Society for the Prevention of Cruelty to Animals
RSVP	please reply (réspondéz s'il vous plaît)
S	
S, Sth	south
s.a.e.	stamped addressed envelope
S.A.S.	Special Air Service
Sat.	Saturday
SE	south-east
Sept.	September
St	Saint; street
Sun.	Sunday
SW	south-west
T	
tbsp.	tablespoon
temp.	temperature
Thurs.	Thursday
tsp.	teaspoon
Tues.	Tuesday
TV	television
U	
U.F.O	Unidentified Flying Object
UK	United Kingdom
UN	United Nations
USA	United States of America
UV	ultraviolet
V	
V.I.P.	Very Important Person
v	versus
W	
Wed.	Wednesday
wk	week

100 difficult words to spell

English

which	can't	guess	they
their	sure	says	half
there	loose	having	break
separate	lose	just	buy
don't	Wednesday	doctor	again
meant	country	whether	very
business	February	believe	none
many	know	knew	week
friend	could	laid	often
some	seems	tear	whole
been	Tuesday	choose	won't
since	wear	tired	cough
used	answer	grammar	piece
always	two	minute	raise
where	too	any	ache
women	ready	much	read
done	forty	beginning	said
hear	hour	blue	hoarse
here	trouble	though	shoes
write	among	coming	tonight
writing	busy	early	wrote
heard	built	instead	enough
does	colour	easy	truly
once	making	through	sugar
would	dear	every	straight

English

_____   _____

_____   _____

_____   _____

_____   _____

_____   _____

_____   _____

_____   _____

_____   _____

_____   _____

_____   _____

_____   _____

_____   _____

_____   _____

_____   _____

_____   _____

_____   _____

General knowledge

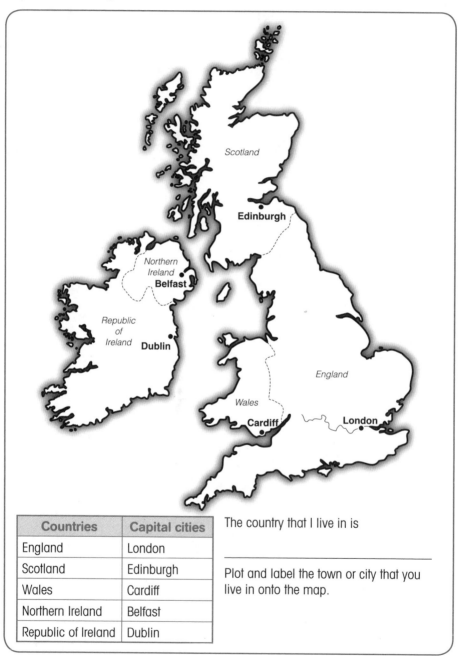

Countries	Capital cities
England	London
Scotland	Edinburgh
Wales	Cardiff
Northern Ireland	Belfast
Republic of Ireland	Dublin

The country that I live in is

_____

Plot and label the town or city that you live in onto the map.

General knowledge

Colour the flags in their correct colours.

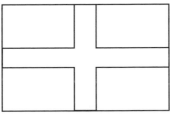

England

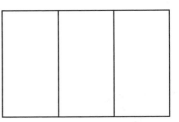

Northern Ireland

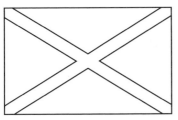

Scotland

Republic of Ireland

Wales

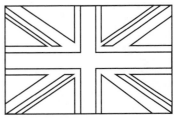

United Kingdom

Area
England .... 130 423 km²
Scotland .... 78 772 km²
Wales .... 20 766 km²
Northern Ireland .... 14 121 km²
Republic of Ireland .... 70 282 km²

Population
England 53 012 456
Scotland 5 254 800
Wales 3 063 456
Northern Ireland 1 810 863
Republic of Ireland 4 581 269

General knowledge

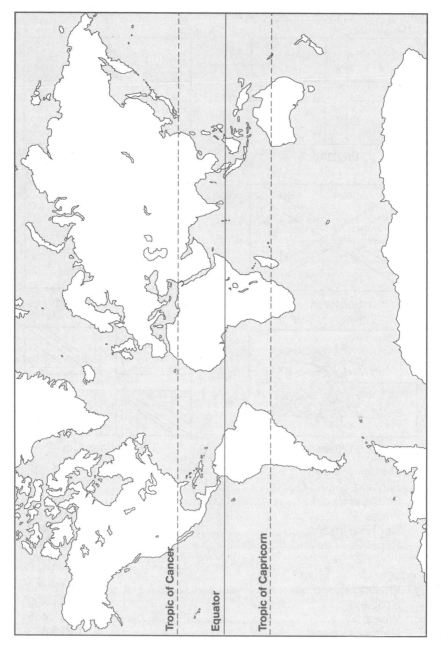

Tropic of Cancer

Equator

Tropic of Capricorn